CAPSULE
STORIES

Masthead
Natasha Lioe, Founder and Publisher
Carolina VonKampen, Publisher and Editor in Chief

Cover art by Matthew Torres
Book design by Carolina VonKampen

Paperback ISBN: 9781734324662
Ebook ISBN: 9781734324679

CAPSULE STORIES

Summer 2020 Edition

Published exclusively by Capsule Stories

Contents

Letters from the Editors

Ironically enough, I write this letter from the gate at an airport that feels deserted and eerie, wearing a face mask and obsessively washing my already cracked and dry hands. I am about to embark on a cross-country drive from Florida to California, my first time driving across the country, for a reason that would take too long to explain, a problem that I must solve myself. My life has taken turns that have been unexpected, disappointing, never meeting up to my dreams or expectations. But I will move forward. I must. It is the only thing to do.

—Natasha Lioe, Founder and Publisher

The best summer job I had was working at a law firm. Every afternoon, I got to run errands. Some days I'd take a stack of envelopes and make deliveries on foot in Cedar Rapids' small downtown area, but most days, I got to drive around in my car, dropping off packages and letters at offices. It was a blast. I'd ride around town, listening to new music, letting my mind wander, thinking about moving to college in the fall. Figuring out how to keep going forward even though everything was changing. Moving forward one day at a time, one errand at a time.

Today, time doesn't seem so straightforward, even though it's summer and the days are getting longer. Time has slowed and sped up erratically in the pandemic; the weekdays and weekends blur together; weeks go by in a flash. It's hard to know how to move forward when we're stuck inside, unsure what the future brings, unable to plan much further ahead than a week or two.

The poems and prose in *Capsule Stories* Summer 2020 Edition explore the ways in which we go forward, from walking around your neighborhood and speeding along the highway

---

to reflecting on the past in order to move on, moving forward from heartbreak or loss, getting up off the ground when we fall down. We hope you enjoy this edition of *Capsule Stories* and find in it the words you need to keep going forward, one day at a time.

—Carolina VonKampen, Publisher and Editor in Chief

keep moving forward

Going Forward

The sun beats down, the light reflecting off the cars around you. The breeze whips through the car windows as you drive through the windy path around the coast, the ocean's waves licking the shore a few hundred feet below you. You have decided that you can no longer stay where you are. It's time to go. Anywhere but here. You're escaping from the people who have held you back for too long. You've been cut down and broken down, and you won't let anyone stop you this time. You travel, through dusty highways and past sandy coasts, through forest paths and thick downtown traffic. It all passes by in a blur, and before you know it, the sun turns the sky a deep purple, and the green trees you've learned to look up to start to look burnt as the leaves turn orange and dry.

You keep going forward. There isn't any other choice.

An Overheated Submarine Takes Us from Press Club to South Delhi

Uttaran Das Gupta

Past Raisina Hill's gradient, bureaucratic
sandstone domes sunk in yellow light; past circles,
endless, once indecipherable, concentric;
past branches grabbing at fog-ropes, symptomatic
of the dirt in our lungs; past the purple
jacaranda canopy. At this hour, static
roads rearrange themselves into dramatic
maps, like a clock's insides, like an aquatic
landscape, precarious, sparking cartographic
curiosity: through what automatic
process did these routes become so familiar,
confusing for the driver; to me, so clear?

This 2 a.m. Uber, a warm submarine,
called by an algorithm to escort us
through this urban aquarium. Every screen
frosted in this overheated submarine
distorts perspective. Blowers, superfluous,
make civic furniture flower into marine
items: sunk aircraft carriers, dogs turning green,
sprouting piranha gills. This hot submarine
shoots across this Atlantis like a time machine,
overfamiliar with the labyrinthine
fold of the ocean floor. Blind crabs of the night,
scuttle away, half in fear, half delight.

May is myopic. The smallness of it all:
fill the bottles, dry your clothes, take out the garbage;
buy vegetables: eggplant, beetroot, peas; call

your mother. Tepid light grows on your windows, falls
with an inalterable rhythm: cabbage
days. The clockwork is unsound, rusty. You crawl
through mushroom hours; the amaltas grows pall.
An in-between month, a technical snag that stalls
the metro in a tunnel. Cylindrical walls
enclose zombie-thoughts, like a stillborn's caul.
Everything is too sanitized here, the skies
need some smoke, some ink. You need gluttonous eyes.

static
roads rearrange
themselves
into
dramatic
maps

Overfamiliar

Uttaran Das Gupta

You came, went—it didn't even register,
like spring comes now only to Lodhi Road,
Mughal Gardens, ignoring the pin code
where your postcard found this subeditor
once, with typos and half-truths in his hair.
Where from? Zangsti. *Go to the hills*, you wrote.
To the hills? *Yes, the perfect antidote
for your condition is the mountain air.*
Ignoring this romantic prescription,
I've remained half-fearful, half-skeptic,
embroiled in pragmatic preoccupations
of budgets, elections, growing seasick.
What maps do I need? Should my backpack be light?
. . . Tickets? ISBT is shut for the night.

Summer returns like a dry tongue, whiplash,
turning the bougainvillea into dust;
the warm water accelerates the rust
on pipes; a lethargic dusk rots the trash
on my stairs. We take an auto to Khan
Market—no conversation, you smoke;
overfamiliar Lodhi Road chokes
potential desire: dehydration.
We learn to survive endless, rainless days,
as medieval waters evaporate
from Agrasen. The comfortable space
between us—Malviya to Saket—helps negate
the possibility of a heatstroke
that listless August can provoke.

Rowboat: Christmas Cove, Maine 1962

Lucy Tyrrell

When I tie my life jacket
over my blouse and pedal pushers,
I transform into kapok pumpkin,
diameter of my skinny sunburned arms and legs
barely thicker than the oars I clutch as wood
shafts tower above my ten-year-old frame.

I look down, steeply angled, to low tide.
A circle of gray-bottomed rowboats
drifts on lines snug-tied back and forth
on cleats around the floating dock,
like parental reminders—repeated more than once.

Wind shifts the water space between boats
like hulled cards fanned for inspection.
I step down the sand-painted plank,
one hand firm on rope railing.

Gripping gunwale, I step onto the wooden
floorboards of my aunt's dinghy, perch
my skinny frame on center thwart,
sink oars in oarlocks—ready to row.

Released from the dock,
I brace my slender legs
against painted planks, clutch rough grips.
Oarlocks rattle with each pull.

I delight in the bright ripple-wake
behind the boat and in wheeling gulls
laughing with joy.

Looking over my shoulder to steer,
I row toward the naked masts of sailboats
that wind-pull against anchors,

toward islands of ragged spruce
above exposed granite slabs.

The dock gets smaller
pull by pull. It is only

a small journey,
but it is a gift,

the lightness
of unmoored

adventure.

a small journey

is a gift

Easing Out
the Clutch

Larry Pike

after Michael Pettit

Mom signaled, though no one followed our little car,
and turned into the big Baptist church's parking lot,
newly sealed but not yet restriped, where she drifted

to the center of a black hole of asphalt, shifted
into neutral, tapped the brakes once or twice,
and stopped. I considered her from the passenger's side

as she set the hand brake and said, opening her door
and stepping out, "Switch places." I couldn't move
as she curved around the bumper to stand beside me,

waiting for me to surrender my seat, saying nothing else,
demonstrating not so much patience as resolve, until
I hunkered past, circling to the other side. Wanting to drive

and wanting to learn to drive are different urges. Mom could
put me behind the wheel, but she couldn't make me ease out
the clutch gently until I could sense the engine surge.

"Give it gas, but not so much at once, you'll feel it in your feet,"
she coached, then shut up and sat back. My pulse accelerated.
In her place Dad would have kept instructing, micromanaging,

expecting a fluid transfer of energy, a smoother roll
across the expanding pavement. I would have learned more
from him than how to drive—mechanics of the differential,

thermodynamics of internal combustion—maybe valuable
info for later, but Mom just had me try. Of course
I stalled and bucked, but soon we were maneuvering

through suddenly open frontier down Friendly past Ham's
to West Greenway on wide whitewalls in the boxy Fiat 1100,
four doors, four on the tree, forever a ground gear from freedom.

forever a ground gear from
freedom

Gravel Road

Arianna Sebo

Sweaty and hot
taxed
fatigued
fuzzy-headed
driving is difficult
wishing it would rain
bare arms burning in the sun
I drive down the dusty road
raising the roof to the sounds
of Kid Rock and the gravel
hitting my tires

Go, Just Go

Ed Ruzicka

The summer my sister Clare got home from four years
in a liberal arts curriculum at the University of Budweiser,
I had a driver's license and a job at the county airport.
Seated on top of a tractor in 85-degree heat, I mowed
huge swaths of Indian grass, wild rye, thistle.
Mice, rabbits darted, pheasants shot up
as my beastly John Deere cast its shadow
and shuddered along runways, cut a six-foot wide
strip by quarter-mile-long strip seven hours a day.

Those were the best Cokes, eight-ounce bottles
the gang boss ferried out at around 2 p.m.
in a beat-up Ford F100 painted like a yam.
Iced, shot-cold bottles tipped upside down.
Run fast down a throat scratchy as hay
under a sun that tried to teach me what it takes
to be relentless, naked, generative without pause.

Come Saturday Clare and I, bored out of our ever-loving minds,
would drive to auto lots along Ogden Avenue.
Pretend we were in the market for this GTO,
that crouching red Cougar. Guys in starched shirts
and a gas-cloud of spray-on deodorant would
have to stuff their *Playboys* into side drawers,
swing loafers down off the desk, toss on a lime and pumpkin,
plaid sports coat. Then hoof it out into summer heat.
After we gave them our licenses to hold,
and fully against their better judgement,
they grudgingly forked over keys to spanking new machines.

Off we'd spin. Crank that radio. Find the Stones or 'Retha on
there.
"Goose it, Clare! Give it something. See what's under the hood."
Back then punks were made to go places. It was one way
of telling ourselves we weren't going to spend the rest
of our lives tasting farm dust. So we flamed out
large mazes around these lots. Circled them like we were
buzzards floating high on top of fabulous fountains of wind
over an endless range of mountains called future, called fate.

Off we'd spin

Bad Work

Ed Ruzicka

Sometime in the Seventies
I saw Volvos start to pop up
at city stoplights
with drop-dead beauties
framed in window glass.

Then I danced with one
dressed as a de Kooning
at a party thrown by an art professor.
Paula. Paula could shimmy,
could hesitate fragile as ash
for one drum beat
at the end of my grasp
then sail in, swirl under
my uplifted arm.

Soon we started to drive out
to a bar pit by the interstate.
We'd lurch toward that lake
through a quarter mile of twists,
crusted ruts, slop. Volvo headlights
lit on armadillos under shrubbery.

We'd smoke some weed, down wine.
Lay out suspended, bare,
in star-touched waters
as tree tops rimmed our vision.

Eighteen wheelers barreled
through distant interstate pitch.

Relieved of gravity, we drifted
like compass needles held fast
by the true north of a magnetism
that arises in the bodies of lovers.

A few months later, living together
in the sacrament of our hope,
her Volvo's brakes started to squeal.
I said we could save a bundle
if I replaced the pads myself.
I crouched, knelt, grunted,
lay on my back.
I threw all I had
into splitting asunder
nuts fused to bolts
by thousands of miles
of furious motion.
Down driveway concrete
I laid parts out in radiant rows.
She fixed a sandwich with chips.
Brought me ice water.

With gritty determination,
I wrenched it back together
but didn't understand a thing
about fluid or pressure.
So the next day
Paula flew through the stop sign
at the end of our street
into a vacant lot big enough
that she could run the Volvo
down in circles.

The crazy thing was
how she forgave me.
Later that year we married.
For various reasons
more complicated
than any mechanical work,
I mucked that up, too.
Before we separated
the Volvo's engine froze,
so the car got replaced
by the most practical, boring tin can
this skinflint could find
in the wanted ads.

Our divorce gave me that car.
I did nothing but go to work
and back for a long time.
I eased my foot off the gas,
hugged my lane.

I Hitchhiked
All Over

Ed Ruzicka

Weeds up through a rusting Chevy
whose hood yawned for no reason
other than laziness in country shade.
An enamel freezer on a porch
beside a seat unbolted from a Chevy,
then set as an outside couch where a man
could pass the night, smoke, keen for owls,
piss beer just beyond pine boards.

Riverbed swaddled in cottonwood.
Arroyo run down from mountain snow.
That mountain turning in the distance
somewhere between blue and purple
as the sun fizzles on the horizon.

Woman in a lipstick red dress with
huge polka dots, hose and high heels
stuffing notes into her purse
as she steps out of the State Bank.

It all had the same weight to me.
I needed it bad. All of it.
Had to get to everywhere fast.

I stuck out my thumb. Waited.
Some goober jerked his pickup
to the side. I ran to catch him.
"Where you going?" he'd ask.

I'd talk up a trucker by a gas pump.
He'd say, "I can get ya far
as the Oklahoma line for sure."
"You're gunna have to crouch way down
outta sight if I spy a company man."
"Where ya headed anyhow?"

I always told 'em
"Up the road a-ways."

*Had to get to every-
where fast*

Fort Knox, Labor Day 1985

Bruce Pemberton

A bus drops me off after lights out,
as another trainee, as we're called,
guides me by flashlight to an empty
bunk. I get a new green towel and
a bar of soap. First call is zero six
three zero hours, he tells me, and
I don't know what that means, or
what first call means, either. There's
a latrine, not a bathroom, near my
bunk, with six toilets in a row and
no government funding wasted on
privacy. Large fans move moist air
as I sweat all night, uncertain if I'm
awake or asleep. Lights come on at
six-thirty and an officious voice
announces get up, get dressed, you
have ten minutes to make your bunk,
and get outside, we're moving to
chow. We don't know how to march
yet, so we walk quickly to the nearby
mess hall and form a line. The first
few attempt to order omelets and
get yelled at. You don't have time
for those, you get scrambled, bacon,
hash browns, two pancakes, and
a carton of milk or juice. Stick and
move, men, stick and move, double-
time back to the barracks, and we
discover that means run. Later,
we'll get uniforms, boots, haircuts,

shots, and briefings that'll border
on the profane. Still dark out, there's
the last crescent, low in the east and
yellow, barely there. Any other time,
I'd stop for an eyeful. I'm uncertain
how long it'll be before I'm able to
admire a simple crescent moon again.

Any other time, I'd stop for an eyeful

Fort Bragg, California 2018

Brian Rihlmann

Almost twenty years ago, it was,
I drove this same hairpin highway
following a full moon
west through the redwoods
in early morning darkness,

and today,
on the eve of my forty-fifth trip
around the wheel,
I arrive here yet again
and stand at cliff's edge
looking out over the same ocean,
different waves
crashing into the rocks below,

as the same moon,
now barely half,
hangs overhead
like a curved blade
and the sun rises
at my back.

The moon may have
leaked half away,
but the day is wide
as the dome of sky
growing deeper blue,
and the sea with it,
as the sun climbs,

warming my shivers,
casting its first shadows,

like that fisherman
on the beach below,
casting his first line
of the day,
with chilly hope
and a smile.

same ocean,

different waves

Outer Banks

Stacy Alderman

Drive me down
to Highway 12
drop me off
on the northern beaches
I'll roam with the
wild mustangs
and bathe in the surf
let the salt breeze
dry my hair
I'll wander down
to the town of Duck
wade into the sound
glide gently on a kayak
till I reach Kitty Hawk
climb soft, sandy dunes
where the Wright Brothers flew
gaze over the horizon
to Kill Devil Hills
where pirates smuggled booze
swim toward Nags Head
green, blue tumbling surf
I can almost see the lantern
hanging from the neck of a nag
as it paces the dunes
Sleep in the shadow
of modest Bodie Island Light
detour to Manteo
quiet little town
calm waters of Roanoke
glistening in the sun

---

back to the highway
its narrow two lanes
the ribbon grows thinner
as I push my way south
pay my respects
to the graveyard
out at sea
the landscape grows sparse
the closer I move
toward the Hatteras giant
black and white brick
a towering beacon
at the edge of the world

drop me off
on the northern beaches

Outer
Banks II

Stacy Alderman

Rise in the darkness
the sun still asleep
coffee and suitcases
being pulled east
mountains and highways
a grin on your mouth
five hundred miles
being pulled south
over the causeway
sea birds and sky
why ever leave here
why even try
cruise down the beach road
wind in your hair
waves on the sand
salt in the air
dolphins at sunrise
hammock and breeze
heart is at peace
soul is at ease
seafood and ice cream
golden brown tan
roll in the waves
lounge in the sand
climb up the lighthouse
play in the dunes
somehow it's always
over too soon
tears with the sunrise
on the last day
one day you know
you'll be here to stay

U-Turn

Steve Denehan

Things are rarely as bad
or as good
as they seem
one minute you are driving
the streetlights pulsing by
music blaring
throat ragged from the singalong
then the phones rings
bad news
the worst news
one U-turn later
the car is silent
the streetlights insipid
the road a salty blur

good is temporary
bad is temporary
everything in between is temporary
every silver lining has a cloud
but summer hides in every snowflake

Burn Out

Sarra Culleno

Impetus.
A meteor
is down-hurtling
toward a goal, or target
(we can't tell which).

The atmosphere tears
its layers: friend, lover,
health, temper, all frazzle.
Integer lost.

The chunks of I fly
in a tail of sky behind.
The flaming circles
are beautiful trails above

until momentum's lost.
It is not hurtling.
It is a floating speck of ash
going nowhere.
Inertia.

Waiting for the Light to Change

John Grey

I'm transported too often, that's my problem.
I can't stay with this avenue, this streetlight.
I'm in a jet, with Alex, flying high above the city.
I'm parked outside Dawn's apartment building,
I'm in the motel swimming pool, keeping my head above
the sparkling green water, watching Jennifer grace
her dripping back with a white fluffy towel.
It's red light for now but green for every other time.
So here I go backtracking the trail left by a cliché
to where it was inevitably true.
And always the rain falling.
I curse this weather. I used to take it to heart.
Windshield wipers now, a giddy laugh then.
And I'm on the way home from work.
But it feels like after midnight.
I have to pick up some groceries.
But my list says,
parking at the lookout, the drive-in,
the club, the loud music, the wild dancing.
Light changes. A circle of pale emerald.
I struggle to get going again.
The past doesn't want me to leave.
The guy behind me toots his horn.
A gesture comes to mind
but not to my middle finger.
I'm like a method actor these days,
playing a role in someone else's play.
My name is goodbye and the next act
is the sound of my car moving forward.

self-care

Kali Richmond

I walk into the slither edge
of the wardrobe door
little toe ricocheting
bent 90-degree grotesque

wear a hole in my palm
thanks to the repetitive rub
of the spade as I'm weeding
I push on for some hours
until the skin is clean gone
leaving damp red wrongness
a stigmata welt
flecked with soil and microbes

I drive and I drive
eight hours
despite my inexperience
there are close shaves
derived from blind spots
febrile anxiety
stops me turning on the radio
I drive
gauche dread my companion
wrists cracking
hold myself cadaver stiff
I refuse to answer the phone
eschewing responsibility

Somewhere

Mark Martyre

Somewhere between an exhausting day
and a torturous night,
I leave my room for a walk.

Perfect weather
on this darkening summer evening.

The weather, the lights, the breeze
breathes
new life, new hope,
new love
into the streets,
the city,
the people.

And hand in hand
I see them on benches
or walking the promenade.

Hand in hand
I see them
at the fruit markets,
rocking on porches,
drinking on patios,

licking ice cream, petting dogs,
laughing, talking,
hugging,
smiling.

And hand in my pockets
I walk around, and behind,
and past them.
Finally turning the corner,
and making my way up
Palmerston Avenue.

The old streetlamps line and light the way
in a hauntingly beautiful row.

The old houses,
the front windows come to life.
I imagine the scenes playing
behind each curtain.

The trees, now in full bloom,
glowing from the moon above,
and the old streetlamps below.

It's the kind of moment worth writing about.
Worth smiling about.
Worth
sighing about.

I made it back to the apartment,
up the small steps,
back to the small room,
back somewhere between an exhausting day
and a torturous night.

And I just had to tell you about it.

And I just had to tell you about it.

A Note
for R.

Mark Martyre

Y'know, I have to say,
sitting here with my coffee,
after running some errands,
preparing for yet another move
and more out-of-one-suitcase living,
that it does feel good to shed the weight
of that collected dust
and be rid of the few things I've caught
in my net, along the way,
and release it all back to the sea.

There's a peace now
in re-minimalizing things
and taking just the bare essentials.
A stack of good books,
a collection of music,
my notebooks, and the clothes on my back.
A hat for the changing season,
and you.

You, you,
you.

Honeymoon

Elizabeth Jaeger

Decision

"You can choose the destination," I told Kati. We were getting married in the spring and had started to think about a honeymoon. "I have just two requirements: we need to use our passports, and it has to be somewhere I've never been."

Luggage

"I used to laugh at people pulling one of these," I grumbled as we wove our way through the crowded airport, pulling our suitcases with wheels behind us. This was a first for me. I was used to carrying a backpack.

"This is a real vacation," she reminded me. Real meaning everything had been mapped out, planned meticulously. We had an itinerary, hotel and tour reservations, and a car rental. While I was well accustomed to international travel, this was all new territory for me, and I felt jittery, fake, perhaps made of plastic.

Backpackers

Our hotel in San José had a bar, a real classy bar, with top-shelf liquor and imported wine. At night, after dinner, Kati and I would relax with a glass of pinot grigio. We'd sit outside in the cool evening air and talk about our dreams for the future—moving to New England, having kids, getting published. While we chatted, my eyes continuously wandered to the hostel across the street. Occasionally, the voices of backpackers—people younger than me, bent over beneath the weight of the packs—would drift toward us. Guidebooks in hand, sweat matting down their hair, they'd ring the bell and inquire as to whether or not there was a vacancy.

"Would you rather be there?" Kati asked, a mournful look in her eyes, as if I were staring at another woman, instead of a rundown building.

I shrugged. "Maybe. Part of me. I guess." It wasn't that I didn't want to be with her. But I couldn't shake the feeling of being displaced. As if I were posing, pretending to be somebody I wasn't.

Tortuguero

Tortuguero National Park was the reason Kati had chosen Costa Rica. She loved turtles and wanted to see them nesting. The lodge in which we stayed was rustic and quaint. The towels in our room were twisted into twin swans. Beautiful birds who mate for life.

We took a walk on the beach, looking for turtle tracks, evidence that the females had begun laying their eggs. A wave crashed, the tide surged over the sand, washing over our feet. Kati grabbed my arm, shock settling into a smile. The ocean accented her blue eyes glinting in the sun.

Later, when darkness fell, we went back to the beach, red lights strapped to our heads as we followed the guide. In absolute silence, we crouched by a mother turtle, her hind legs kicking up sand as she dug a hole. As we bent over to watch, she carefully covered her eggs. Her maternal duties complete, she returned to the sea.

Boxers

My underwear mortified her. Every night, I'd take a shower and then wash my boxers in the bathroom sink. I didn't need to. When we packed—according to her rules, which included a change of clothes per day—I neatly folded then rolled several pairs of underwear. However, through years of traveling, washing and wearing had become a deeply ingrained habit. Once I wrung the water out of them, I tossed them over the balcony railing or out the window to dry. It's what backpackers do—without shame. But apparently, staying in real hotels meant playing by different rules. And those rules included keeping one's underwear unseen by others. A rule I repeatedly broke, until Kati could only laugh. A mask behind which to hide. But from what was she hiding: The humiliation of my boxers fluttering in the wind like a flag for all to see? Or the embarrassment of traveling with someone who so obviously didn't fit in?

Arenal Volcano

Gray clouds swirled around Arenal's peak. Fearing rain, we debated whether or not we should postpone our hike. But it was still early, and since there wasn't much else to do, we decided to go. The sign at the park entrance read, "Active volcano: In the event of an eruption do not breathe noxious gases." Despite the warning, we chuckled, envisioning ourselves holding our breath and running for cover. How long could we go? Thirty seconds? Possibly forty? Even if we pulled off our shirts and breathed into the fabric, how much would that help?

When our laughter subsided, we heard bubbling. Faintly, at first, but the closer we got to the volcano, the louder it became. It sounded like the pudding I made with my mother as a child. She always poured the milk, but I added the powder from the box. As the milk warmed on the stove, it thickened, until it started to boil. Boiling pudding sounds much different—deeper, thicker, more muted—than boiling water. Used to hiking back home in New York, we pondered the possibilities. What could be making such a strange sound? The obvious answer eluded us, until we reached a second posted sign: "Danger. Area of high volcanic activity. No trespassing."

"Lava!" It finally clicked. The bubbling sound we heard was hot lava boiling beneath the ground. It was then we realized the gray clouds churning above were not storm clouds at all, but smoke billowing up from the bowels of the earth.

Rappelling

Rappel through waterfalls! Kati saw the excursion advertised in our hotel and was drawn by the novelty of it. We had no other activity planned for the day, and since I'm always game for outdoor adventures, I readily agreed to sign up when she suggested it. No prerequisite skills or experiences were required. We hiked to a series of waterfalls. At each one, our guide set up the equipment. We slid into our harnesses. Neither one of us had ever been climbing or rappelling. The concept was new, though I have always picked up athletic tasks quickly, my body easily adapting to what is necessary. As I jumped from the top of the waterfall, adrenaline, like a drug, rushed through me, the cold water shocking my skin until I eased into it. I caught myself, my feet bracing against the rock face until I settled in the rhyme of rappelling. The spray washing over me was invigorating. Kati, less graceful, slipped in one of the falls, her shin slamming against the jagged stone, blood trickling down. With a slight wince she rubbed the bruise. The soon-to-be scar that she'd flaunt like a medal, a souvenir of our marriage, perhaps a foreshadowing of the future.

The Broken Bridge

The road from Arenal to Monteverde was treacherous. Not a single stretch was paved. I drove no faster than thirty miles per hour, and even that was probably too fast. Holes the size of the windshield pitted the road. Kati sat beside me. Even with the seatbelt clicked across her chest, she bobbed up and down like the needle of a sewing machine.

More than halfway to our destination, we came to a river. Once upon a time a bridge crossed the water, but all that remained were two planks of wood. I slammed on the brakes, a cloud of dust swirling behind me. It looked as though the car tires could rest easily upon the planks, but I'd have to align the car perfectly. And even if I could do that, could I trust them to hold the weight?

I glanced over at Kati. She shrugged. As if our success in crossing were entirely dependent upon an optimistic attitude. But before I could respond, a young man, perhaps a teenager, appeared on the opposite bank. Holding his arms up, he waved, flagging my attention. With his hands, he signaled for me to move forward. Then he guided me, his hand turning right, then left, until I heard a rattling sound—tires making contact with the wood. Then slowly, afraid to nudge the wheel even a quarter of an inch, in case the tires broke contact with the planks, I drove until the river was behind me. Rolling my window down, I held out a few bills, a thank you for granting me safe passage. But as the young man smiled in return, I wondered what happened to the bridge. Had it been washed out by a flash flood? Had it decayed from lack of maintenance? Or had the locals simply envisioned a way to make money?

Monteverde

We went to Monteverde for the zip lines, despite my aversion to heights. Mostly, we zoomed across one at a time, exhilaration zipping through me, displacing fear as we raced high above the tree line. But toward the end, the guide instructed us to double up. One of the lines was best done in tandem. Three-quarters of the way across our momentum slowed, then stopped. Wrapping my legs around Kati, I swung around. Then hand over hand, I swiftly pulled her to the finish.

Dirty Clothes

The goal had been to bring enough clothes to last the duration of the trip, but we both fell short. Somewhere toward the end of our holiday, having gathered a few sweaty T-shirts and some dirty underwear, Kati slogged into the bathroom to wash them—*by hand*.

I had learned to wash by hand years before on my very first excursion abroad, and since then, I had done it enough that I could do it quickly and efficiently. However, Kati, like many Americans, had relied upon a washing machine her whole life. To wash by hand was a new, startling experience. While she washed, I sat outside on the deck and read. She didn't have much to do, so I didn't expect it to take long. But after nearly an hour, when my stomach started to rumble, I decided I should probably check on her. Poking my head into the bathroom, I found her slumped on the floor, tears flowing copiously down her cheeks. The wet, soapy clothes languishing in the sink. In exasperation, I sighed. But neither scolding her nor comforting her was going to get me to dinner anytime soon. And because I desperately wanted to eat, I washed her clothes—scrubbing, beating, rinsing, and wringing. When I hung them to dry, her mood vastly improved, and even though there was more than one pair of underwear flapping in the night air, she didn't complain.

New York Pizza

I love beans. Kati does not. In Central America, beans are a staple. In Costa Rica, gallo pinto—a simple rice and black bean dish—is everywhere. When we stayed in Tortuguero, the resort served it on the buffet during breakfast, lunch, and dinner. Still accustomed to traveling cheaply, holding onto my money and seeing how far I could stretch it, beans were beautiful. I could eat until my stomach cried uncle, and pay very little. But the beans that made me smile left Kati feeling famished. For her, eating became a daily challenge. The thought *will I find something I like* quickly devolved into *will I find something I can tolerate*. Too often the answer came back—loudly as it echoed through the restaurant—*NO!* This quest for edible food, something that would not make her gag, ended in a puddle of tears, a meltdown one evening when she ordered pizza in a restaurant. Pizza. How could you go wrong with pizza? Very easily. All too often when abroad, the word pizza is used far too liberally to describe anything made from a foundation of dough, topped with a reddish sauce (usually, though not always, tomato based) and a sprinkling of something cheesy. That night, hope sparkled in her eyes—she hadn't eaten for two days—but the hope died an instant death, snuffed out by a single bite. It barely resembled pizza; it tasted more like chalk on a brick.

The following day, entering the beach town of Manuel Antonio and driving down the main road, she caught sight of a restaurant, the sign outside advertising New York-style pizza. The brakes slammed. The car came to an immediate stop. And I knew what we were having for lunch. It certainly didn't taste like New York. But nothing outside of New York ever does. It was, however, not bad. Which meant bye-bye beans, because Kati was tired of starving. For the rest of our holiday we filled up on nothing but pizza.

The Storm

The night before we were scheduled to fly home, we had to drive back to San José. Kati drove slowly in the dark—there were no streetlights to guide her—navigating her way through the narrow, windy roads. Then suddenly, the clouds that had been hovering all day unleashed a rain similar to the rains I had experienced in Korea during monsoon season. It was like driving through a waterfall, only there was no breaking through to the other side. The windshield wipers couldn't keep the rain off the windshield. Kati slowed the car even more. Her knuckles on the wheel shined white against the darkness, and she started to hyperventilate. The moment she saw a parking lot, she pulled into it. She was shaking.

"We'll wait it out," she said on the verge of tears as she turned off the engine. And we tried. But the rain showed no sign of stopping.

"I'll drive," I finally said.

"No, it's too dangerous," she argued, panic clear and sharp in her voice. But she realized we had no other option. Taking a deep breath, she handed me the keys but held my hand for a brief moment. "Are you sure?" she asked. I nodded, and when she let go of my hand we pushed the doors open, stepped out into the pouring rain, and ran around the car to switch seats. We needed to keep moving, pushing forward together despite the storm; only then would we reach our destination.

pushing forward together despite the storm

This Morning

John Grey

Yawns nudge against the shallow darkness,
sky, a gold cloud-mass with patience.
No more night or dreams, and women
are as long as they are beautiful,
even man, that silent ship, floats a little
on the black-beard stubble of his own loveliness
as she flickers her eyes from death to life
as, for every dawn, existence is much stronger,
all in the growing of exultation and of the earth,
blood perfect red like the sweet pea,
as life weighs itself, not in gravity but lips,
the first brush, lovers in and out of each other's eyes,
as light arrives, speaks its verdict in a hug,
time rests a moment, trembles, before moving on.

Platonic Beach

Maina Chen

I don't know why I want to go to the beach
the place I've hated and avoided as much as I could
I don't know why I imagine myself in a dress
the garment I never thought I was feminine enough to wear
outside
I can't stop thinking about how you're next to me
but we don't hold hands
we don't touch
we don't talk
we don't need to
the ocean, repeatedly crashing over itself
says enough
and does all the speaking for us

Flying Away

Michelle M. Mead

She found the keys to summer in the running away
Because there is more to learn in cobblestone cracks
On sidewalks in foreign places, places farther away
Than the next state over or the same old beach town

Boarding the plane cut the ties that held her
Opening the skies, the world, the adventures yet to be
Why waste time sitting on the beach and burning,
Sand sticking to every part of your lotioned-up body

No, it had to be a stretch—of the mind, body, soul
There was no growth in looking back and holding on
To the teenage dreams of tanned boys on the shore
No, the growth came in going forward—
In the freeing moment of flying away.

Walking Tour

Dani Castonzo

Your ex has her nipples pierced, and I am the kind of girl who only talks about getting her nipples pierced. So I wake up, hungover and sleepy, and I dare myself to walk 20 miles.

I pack the essentials: notebooks, pen, chorizo, backup pen, a Pulitzer Prize–winning novel, slightly old cheese, sunscreen, ointment for the road rash on my ass (note that I will never dare myself to go rollerblading again).

I walk all damn day. Sweaty men jog in Casa de Campo through the yellow grass and sparse, piney trees. Battles were fought here. I spit; I imagine it mingling with the blood and spit of Spanish soldiers and give myself chills on a sunny day. Five miles blur by and my feet keep moving. I'm a little bored, a little thirsty. I sit on a picnic bench, one cheek off the seat. "FUCK SOCIALISM" is etched in the table. I am here to write, to make something of this day and this grand adventure my life is supposed to be. But the wheels just turn like the cyclists whipping by, kicking up dust and twigs but no prize-winning words.

I walk to my favorite supermercado. I take my lunch to Palacio Real and sit on a shady bench under a low-hanging tree, where the tourists can't see me and I can't see them, and some dude is playing "Despacito" on the harp and I'm loving the quiet until I realize I'm sitting on a pile of fire ants. I move benches. I watch a couple take selfies for ten minutes. I hear a lot of Spanish, a lot of English ("Honey, what's that art museum called again? The Prawdo?").

12 miles. I sing to myself when I'm on lonely streets. I guess how many miles I've walked. I talk to myself, in Spanish and in English: "Stop overthinking everything all the time." "Está bien, no te preocupes, we're having fun."

I meet a lot of people. An overly-friendly man in the farmacia who asks how much I weigh. A Spanish mother and

daughter who hustle me into buying a terrible, billowy shirt
("¡Mira, guapa, esta camiseta es para ti, te queda tan bien!").
I'm flattered but unhelpful when asked for directions. I stop
and breathe deeply when a cool breeze rushes down the narrow streets.

16 miles. I walk to Retiro, my favorite park in Madrid.
I haven't spoken more than a couple words all day. It's late
afternoon, and my phone has been off for hours. I'm dehydrat-
ed. I imagine you with your guitar walking next to me. I think
about ridiculous things I would say, things I will probably
never say: "You know, I'm very goal-oriented. We should rent
a car and drive out west sometime and I'll write a book and
you can write music and we'll never have to go inside again.
What if we're supposed to be together? You really have to try
this churros place."

Fuck, are my shin splints coming back? Fuck me. Fuck
you. What if we're not good together?

17.5 miles. I buy a tub of laundry detergent. I have to keep
walking, I have to keep moving—two and a half miles to go.
That's nothing. I'm lightheaded and I've picked an inoppor-
tune time to buy detergent.

I walk a couple sluggish blocks. I'm reminded of the des-
perate miles I used to run, sometimes late at night, sometimes
when I was supposed to be in class, sometimes when I hurt
every time my right leg hit the pavement.

Miguel Cervantes stares down at me from the side of
a hipster café on Calle Huertas. "Él que lee mucho y anda
mucho, ve mucho y sabe mucho."

I'm so close.

---

18 miles of walking, talking, singing, and swearing, and I'm at my apartment door. The soles of my feet are sore and my back is damp and the handle of the detergent digs into my fingers.

You really can't run from anything.

Final Curtain

Sarah Marquez

At first, we walked everywhere
on our adventures. Up and down Walnut Street,
admiring the homes hemmed in by giant oaks
and lamp posts; to the high school with the bulldog's
snarling face out front or the corner bakery
and coffee stop; along the boulevard of indie shops
and eateries from around the world—Indian, Italian,
Korean, Mongolian.

The cracked sidewalk slipped under us,
wearing out our sneakers. Our bare legs
tanned in the sun. Once, we left the main road
for gravel and rust-proof fences. We hiked up the hillside
until the city lights were lost in the dust, spinning
miniature tornadoes behind us. I wore a red dress
that day and sat in the purple fountain grass
while you photographed the landscape.

When your new car came in,
the sleek Volkswagen, we named it
Sheila because it was part of us and took us
places we'd never been. Like Point Mugu at sunset.
The blood-orange hues of the horizon reached out
of the sky and inside us. Our toes broke the surface
of the sea, sunk beneath the sand. Little gray crabs
emerged between them. We scooped them up
and watched their wild legs wriggle in midair.

Then you said something I can't remember.
It set me on edge. It could have been *sorry*

---

or *help me*. Sorry, because I walked in on you
drunk the night before. You were sprawled out in the tub,
muttering bad poetry, all cut up and bloody.
Help me, because you needed someone to start caring.
But I never noticed the crablike scars scuttling
across your arms, concealed in a field of golden freckles.

I wonder if you ever think about that overcast afternoon
when Sheila drove us into the mountains. She parked
at the head of a cliff and we got out to stare into the mist
hanging like a final curtain, blocking our view of the land
below and beyond. Everything I meant to say to you
then was stuck behind something just like it, waiting
in the end for a little gravity to tear it down.

waiting
in the end

for a little gravity to tear it down

Salem, Massachusetts 2019

Lynne Schmidt

Originally published in On Becoming a Role Model
by Lynne Schmidt (Thirty West Publishing, 2020)

Lost in the middle of the crowd
my niece asks the tour guide
how they used to hang the witches.

How did they get them to that tree branch?

The tour guide offers options—
a ladder kicked out from beneath,
a rope over a strong limb
while strong men pulled
the world out from under their feet.

Sometimes the neck broke,
sometimes the victim struggled.
Most times, they weren't witches,
just poor people,
eccentric people,
people who decided to
have a voice.

My niece is six years old.
She knows nothing of the world yet.

And I will show her
that they cannot burn us all.

End of July

Alexandre Ferrere

End of July, the
city is way too foggy the
heads too smoky though
we're still in the middle of
an afternoon.
At the window, looking
below my own
suspended body the
seagulls reflect in the
dark puddles, their
brief quest rippled
from time to
time by random
raindrops.
They hanged me so high so
everyone could see
me rotting above
curbed screams the
breast opened to the
street introducing mortal
candor to mortals.
I'm dead already, but
still can't talk.
It's the
end of July.

The Hanged Man

Morgan Russell

Listen.
Universe says,
grab what you can,
run.

Freeze.
Universe says,
misfortune come;
for you didn't run.

Halt.
Universe says,
surrender.

Shift.
Universe says,
you're stuck.
Universe cuts the rope.
Get off the ground.

Endure

Morgan Russell

Twice, you've been torn
from your place;
cut down,
poisoned.
You cannot
fathom the end,
so you grow.

You grow and you find yourself
twined together—
with your environment.
You are
so tired.
The two of you have
grown together.
Harmony was never
the same thing as love.
You're torn to the ground
under the hot, unforgiving sun.

In the right environment
you are considered
invaluable.
You are kuzuyu,
the fundamental remedy.
There is so much goodness in
what you are.

When they dig their nails into
you underbelly, cutting and pulling,

do not dig deep and hold on
to what sustains you to the
detriment of yourself
and others. You are wild
billowing.

Harmony was never

the same thing as love

The End

Lynne Schmidt

This is how the end feels,
when you're too far inland
to see the tide change,
but too close to the ocean
that salt rusts your car,
the metal of home,
your tongue.
Your teeth are rocks,
cracked against the shoreline
from holding water in your mouth.
You swallow sand
because at least the taste won't make you sick
won't taste like his neck,
won't smell like barefoot nights in starlight.
All these words you promise you'd say
with time.
But time ran out an hour ago,
and here you are alone.

Timing

Gillian Webster

She stands at the bottom of the bed and listens as a truck goes past and then a car. Seconds pass in silence. The sleeping form beneath the covers, a shapeless rise and fall, warm-blooded and breathing.

Finally, the sun hits the spyhole in the door at the perfect angle, sending a rainbow of colored light splashing across the wall and onto the floor. Her heart rate quickens. The need to be outside tugs at her, like a kite string. She eases the door open and slips out through the smallest crack she can make before closing it soundlessly behind her.

As she makes her way down the boardwalk, the air is cool; long shadows cast by the beachfront buildings still block out the light. She's wearing shorts, a faded T-shirt, and a layer of sleep that makes her limbs loose enough that she stumbles when her bare feet hit a spongy board and she weaves a little left and right, touching her fingertips to the rail for balance.

A little farther on and sunlight tickles at the tops of the dunes, climbing faster than she can walk, the way it seems to in summer—as eager as she is to be outside with her feet on the wet sand, down by the shoreline listening to the waves as they tinkle through a shell bank and then hiss with regret over each forced retreat.

She takes a diagonal path today, turning right instead of left. It rained last night and now the sand bears a light sugar crust that is decorated with tiny divots where fat raindrops randomly beat down. The surface was baked dry by the heat of the day rising up through the earth, and so now each step she takes breaks this crust, leaving behind a trail of destruction.

The water, when she wades in ankle deep, is a shock. Cool and refreshing. She squeals quietly to herself, and goose bumps rise on her arms and legs. She remembers how it feels to be a child, only now she is here alone as the sun skims the top of a beach hut, and there's excitement in that, freedom with an edge of danger, alone on this empty beach.

"Lovely morning," a voice says somewhere over her left shoulder, and she lets out a yelp of surprise.

"Sorry. Didn't mean to startle you," the man adds instantly. He holds up his hands in a sign of apology that reads like surrender when he meets her eyes and stares.

She takes a breath and blows it out, ridding herself of the jittery shock. "That's okay. I was just . . ." She holds out her hand to indicate the view because that says it all, no words required.

"I know, right?" the man says. "Perfect time of day to be out here," and he is so right: there's not another soul around.

"My—" She almost says fiancé and then she stops herself. She doesn't question why, just demotes him without thinking. "My boyfriend doesn't get it," she tells this stranger.

"The morning light?" he says like they're in tune, shorthand instantly established by the impressive force of nature surrounding them.

She smiles and nods, amused rather than freaked out by this sudden synchronicity. "All of it. The beach, the light, the air . . . it's so fresh . . . so . . ." She sighs, and her shoulders drop down, down. "It's just so special," she says, not embarrassed to be spilling these secrets to a stranger she only just met.

"And then . . . dolphins," the guy says, pointing. "Look, there they go on their morning swim."

She follows his finger as first one magnificent creature breaks the surface and then another close behind. In the end, there are four of them in this pod. Sunlight sparkles on the glistening curve of their backs and fins, skin slick with water. Mouse gray, she thinks, and then stops herself. No, blue, whale blue. But why compare the color of one mammal to another? They are dolphin blue-gray, a magical color all of their own.

She realizes the man has just said something and she half-turns, a hand over her eyes to shield them from the sunlight. She finds him looking at her curiously, waiting for an answer.

"I'm sorry. I was miles away. Did you say something?" she asks.

"Where do you suppose they go?" he says.

"Who? The dolphins? I—" She stops and smiles. There's a faraway look in the stranger's eyes when he turns again to watch these magnificent mammals breach the surface in search of air. It's a kind of childlike curiosity she decides to indulge. "Well, I imagine them going to work down by the pier. They head out there every morning," she says, which is true, "and then they turn around and come back this way in the afternoon. End of shift."

"And what's their job?" he says, warming to this game of make-believe.

"To catch fish," she says as if it's obvious, which it is.

The man laughs heartily. "Of course. Why didn't I think of that?"

"You're not in tune," she teases because it's clear that he is.

"Hey, I'm in tune," he argues back, flopping down onto the sand, his legs stretched out in front of him, colorful trainers dusted with sand.

She has an option at this point—take the lone walk along the shore that she had intended, or sit down beside this stranger, who feels less like a stranger by the second, and talk. She sits.

The man pulls a shell from the pocket of his running shorts and rolls it in his palm. "Ever seen one of these?" he asks, flattening his hand and holding it out to her.

His palm is pale pink and smooth, bleached almost as if he spends a lot of time in the water. By contrast, the back of his hand is tanned a golden brown. His nails are short and neatly rounded, perhaps from a professional manicure. She takes the speckled brown shell he offers, pinching it between her forefinger and thumb to inspect it.

"Is it a whelk?" she asks.

"Close. It's called an auger," he tells her, watching closely as she rolls the tight spiral between her fingertips. "Careful, that tip can be sharp," he says as she taps the spiky end with the pad of her index finger.

"It's beautiful. How do you know so much about shells?" she asks.

"Goes with the territory. I'm a marine biologist. I work at the marine laboratory," he says, thumbing over his shoulder in the direction of a nearby aquarium and research center.

"Oh. I just assumed you were out here for a run."

The man shakes his head and tips his face up to the sun. "I wish. I came down to check on the sea turtle nests. We're getting near hatching time, so I'm down here every morning as soon as it's light. But I run between each nest if that counts?" he says. "Kind of multitasking."

"And I thought only women could multitask," she jokes.

There is a loaded pause, and then he quietly says, "Maybe you've been hanging out with the wrong men."

His comment is slightly provocative and unknowingly astute. It hits her hard, like being doused in cold water. She sits bolt upright, dusts the sand off her hands and hugs her knees.

The man sits up, too and reaches out to touch her shoulder. "I'm sorry. Did I say something wrong?"

Tight-lipped, she shakes her head. When she offers him a smile, it's watered down. "No. I'm just . . . wrestling with something."

"I get it," he says quickly. "That's one of the reasons I volunteer to come out here. No people, just nature. Less mess."

She feels emotion tighten her chest, choked by his understanding. "Yeah. Things seem so simple out here."

"Maybe they are. Simple, I mean," he says.

She laughs, but it comes out harsher than she intends. "Life's rarely simple. Not in my experience."

No matter what she says, the man is measured and calm, a quality she finds that she likes.

"I'm sorry to hear that," he says. "But you know, maybe it can be . . . if you let it. Just do what feels right out here and throw the rest away."

They sit in silence after that, listening to the waves. Their breathing syncs with the metronomic rhythm of the ocean, chests rising and falling at the same pace, and it's strangely intimate. Like the world is a room with invisible walls and they are inside it together, just being, no need for small talk or any kind of explanation.

After a while, the man clears his throat. "Sorry to get so heavy before. I shouldn't be offering advice. I don't even know you." He pauses before adding, "Except I feel like I kind of do. Is that weird?" His brow is furrowed in confusion.

She pats the sand flat on either side of her feet and then she digs in to feel the silky weight of it when she lifts her hands and lets the tiny grains sift between her fingers. "No. I know what you mean. Me too," she admits.

She looks sideways very quickly, flicking him a glance. His hair is the same sandy color as the beach, a little bleached by the sun, and he is clean-shaven despite the early hour.

"So . . . do you come here often?" the man asks, laughing immediately at his own corny pickup line.

She smiles. "No points for originality, but yes. As often as I can."

The man's eyebrows rise at her cryptic reply. "And can I ask how often that might be?"

She thinks then of her white sundress hanging in the closet, of the two strangers they met in the bar last night and kind of press-ganged into helping them later today, and of the sleeping form in the big white bed. Her something blue will just have to be her mood today. And her something old? Well, that's her story, as old as the hills.

"Not as often as I'd like," she tells him.

The man laughs. He has a nice laugh, she thinks. Not fake or forced. It is a laugh full of joy and surprise, filled with ease. He is an optimist, she decides, based on that little detail alone. He is out of her league.

He looks along the beach when it becomes clear that she has no more to say. The wooden stakes and the orange neon tape surrounding the next turtle nest seem to call to him when they flutter on the breeze, snagging his attention. "Well, I'm here every day at sunrise like I said," he tells her as he stands and dusts the sand off his shorts and the back of his legs.

She pulls her feet beneath her, preparing to get up, and he leans down to offer her his hand, which she grasps, allowing him to pull her upright until they are standing almost toe-to-toe. His hand is as soft as it looked. She can feel his breath on her face when he speaks.

"I'm Greg, by the way," he says, shaking her hand while he still has it.

"Hi, Greg. I'm Leia."

His eyes pop wide with gleeful amusement. "As in Princess?" he asks.

She closes her eyes and groans, but she's smiling, too. "Please don't start."

"Not the first time you've heard that, I'm guessing?" he says, still grinning.

"No. Not the first or the fifty-first. My parents were big fans."

She nods, looking over his shoulder at the big house behind the dunes. It's blindingly white and achingly modern, an ice cube sheathed in sea-green glass. A figure has just appeared out on a balcony.

"But you're not?" he asks, cocking his head to one side as if he is genuinely interested in her reply.

"No, I love the movies. I just . . ." She shrugs, her mind already on weightier things.

"Yeah, I get it," he says. And it seems as if he really does, this strangely intuitive stranger. He clears his throat and takes a step back. "Well, it was lovely to meet you, Leia."

She smiles and scuffs the sand with her bare toes. "Yeah, you too, Greg. Have a great day. Go save those baby turtles."

When her voice catches at the thought of their parting and her eyes bead with surprising tears, she shields them as if from the sun, though she is really hiding from herself. Always hiding from everyone.

He gives her one long last look then he raises his hand in a little wave and begins to walk backward away from her.

Wrong place. Wrong time, she thinks again, watching as the man finally turns his back and jogs off down the beach in search of a staked-out turtle nest, retreating like one of her beloved waves.

She watches him a little longer before she turns and heads back the other way. She jams her hand into the pocket of her shorts, rooting around for the auger shell. She wants to turn around, only she won't. She grips the shell tightly, pressing down on the spiky tip with her thumb until she feels it break the skin.

The sun is hotter now. Sweat trickles down between her shoulder blades. Beneath her hair, her neck and scalp begin to prickle. Her footsteps are leaden. The sand slows her down. Her thighs begin the burn. Blood as red and soft as carnation petals blooms across her skin to form a warm, wet sheen.

The urge to turn around is almost overwhelming.

Almost.

She tightens her grip on the shell and presses harder, swallowing the pain, forcing herself on.

Forward.

One foot in front of the other.

breathing syncs with the metronomic rhythm of the ocean

it's strangely intimate

Before I Go

Akhim Alexis

*"For while my body is careering towards catastrophe, my mind is
elsewhere, concentrated on this other, vital task, which is to tell you
something meaningful before I go." —Cory Taylor*

The morning means nothing without
faint dew moisturizing the trees and
the atmosphere reminding my knees of the temperature.
Zephyr clothes my body as I move toward the shoreline,
momentarily releasing my spirit into the ether, like stardust.
My misgivings interrupted by the pleasure of a peaceful pulse
surrendered to water's edge.
The silk-textured seaweed and crisp saltwater caresses
my collarbone
as I immerse myself into an oceanic womb.
Currents prove my body to be a fragile emblem of intrusion,
as waves lash
in attempts to chase my sangfroid.
Toes tickle mysteriously on the surface of the seabed and act
as a spring
keeping me buoyed and all contours are blurred in exchange
for touristic pleasure.
For now.

Cracks in Our Shadows

Sarah Jane Justice

I.
dirt spreads as an unmarked canvas
you stumble in scattered brush-strokes
guided by a watercolor compass

weak under scratches of canopy,
light is implied by shadows
rushing as smog-built thieves

untethered, they will steal your path
restrained, they will steal your destination

II.
neon light grabs at tired eyes
pulling skin to keep them open
harsh glows force weak pupils to bulge
wide to the views it drowns in blurs

doused in false rays from a pseudo-sun,
you see almost enough
to fear the shroud of blindness

flashing lights guide your feet
to the arrows aimed at your face

III.
tracks bend over broken dirt
weakened by underlying tunnels
roads crumble into ideas of escape

days are laid in repetition
a trail of stone-built insistence
rocks claiming they could never break

you ache to stretch your fingers
to drop your map
to run before it hits the ground

IV.
your path has ended in waves
barking shouts from an angry wind
your name echoed in currents

with closed eyes,
you reclaim your breath
your voice splits the clouds
you see where the road has fallen

you were taught to fear the fire
told bridges burnt would crumble
shown visions of your bones in ash

no longer afraid of flames,
you learned the fear of stagnation
saw rotting planks start falling
beneath feet that lock in place

V.
we echo the frames of bigger lives
walk worn-in paths with open soles
kneel prone in reflected vision

bent under looming shadows,
we start to know our feet
we emerge from copied shapes
shifting to own our stance

our path was laid by others
but our footprints belong to us

salted wounds

Linda M. Crate

i want to
be freed from
winter whose hold
always feels
too long, too hard, too cold;

i don't belong in this frigid
spell of death and stagnant waters—

i need the sun to warm my skin
and to feel the flowers in me bloom again
to see the flowering trees laugh in pinks,
whites, yellows, and purples;

i need to know this reflection is ending
so growth can begin again
when the flowers die so does a part of me

i cannot recall the shape of the sun—

just want the magic of sunlight to warm me
once again and burn winter into submission so
the snow disappears and i am not left here

wrapped in salted wounds and white diamonds of snow.

stagnant waters

Linda M. Crate

i must move forward
leave you behind
in your winter song;
your music
doesn't inspire me anymore—
i am going to bloom
into summer,
and spill over all the places
you said were my
boundaries;
your heart was an obstacle course
i'm no longer interested in
jumping—
there was nothing but silence
and a burden of shared conversations
but never any new magic,
and now that i'm gone
you want me to return to all the places
weighing heavy on my soul;
i cannot go back in time and save the girl
that i once was—
all i can do is fall into spring,
move forward into summer;
because i refuse to stand in your stagnant waters.

Undercloud

A. Martine

It occurred to me
that when you ask me obvious questions,
you may simply be wanting to hear me talk;
like when I let grip loosen on mug handle,
knowing it will fall,
just so I can hear the scintillation,
that shatter-shatter.
Elephantine silences are greedy;
I imagine you must be yearning for the modest
cadences of our conversations,
the sort of thing you get to missing
idly,
even though you shouldn't.

Sunshine, it chases me and I take it personally; at its mercy
on this bed, it means rolling away from the inevitable graze of
it, slow slither of garter snake onto open skin. I close blinds,
arch my neck, contort contort contort till I am *angle droit*,
till I start to think that migrating rooms would take less ef-
fort. I want to scream, but you can't argue with the sun, you
can't argue with something bigger than yourself, though you
have certainly tried. I am reminded of the finger, that one you
wouldn't keep off my thigh—even when I pushed, it bounced
back and all I could do was sigh. It occurred to me that when
you make contact with my skin, you may simply be wanting
to get closer than I'll allow. I am flexible, but I haven't allowed
you much.

And like the shatter-shatter chases the slip of the mug,
like comfortable cadences of tired-but-shared stories,

so, too, do I miss you.
But in a hopeful way,
in a way that is sometimes garish
(or endearing if let be, if I
stop trying so hard to be so cool all the time),
in a way that could make me like summer again
and hate the sun a little, just a little less.

I haven't allowed you much.

City
Seasons

Dani Castonzo

If I don't have you, at least I have the city. Cheering me on when I just barely make the train. Humming along as I sing on a crowded downtown street, thousands of people and not one listening. Sending beautiful city miracles: three walk signs when I'm late for work, a reasonably priced falafel in a gentrifying neighborhood, lingering eye contact with a striking woman on the El. A city where for one night, a roomful of acquaintances can laugh, cheers, and hug like old friends.

If I don't have you this winter, at least I'll have Euchre nights at Nick's, hot mugs of spiced wine at the Christmas market, an excuse to sit at home in slippers cocooned and watching the humidifier breathe life into a room that hasn't felt the sun in days. I have new books to read and poems to write and tears to sob because no one has time to deal with that when the sun is shining on Chicago.

I'll live without you in the spring; it's not my favorite season, but I'll be happy to break out my T-shirts when it hits forty-five again. The world will be gray and green, and I'll splash in muddy puddles on my way to work and take bike rides through undiscovered neighborhoods.

Summer's the best time to be lonely, the nights are shorter. I'll drink a giant beer at a street fest and plunge into the lake, ice cold but forgiving, and I'll make plans on weeknights and watch the city light up at night, building by building, full of people who could feel more or less alone than I do, but I'll never know.

Fall looks like you, in your grays and yellows and turtlenecks, but I'll still make apple baked goods and browse rows of corn and carrots at the farmers market in a light coat. The cool air will capture my breath for the first time in months, and I'll remember how wild it is to breathe in and out. How human to feel lonely in a roomful of people you love and per-

fectly full on the walk home. Each sidewalk crack and scuttling leaf a memory, taking you further from who you once
were, but you're not lost.

you're not lost

I Promise
This Year I'll
Disappear

Kayla King

Some nights I forget. But consider
murmurations to be mandatory
in this truce. Try to justify

the material for portraits
of lost people left
on a thick canvas skin. Make them

real. Hammer out the tin
to find faces. Melt wax to peel
and putty and hold the shape of silhouettes.

Until then, I hope I am greeted with the same
kind of mercy as the shadows we've left
on street corners. I think they still live there.

Even as we age and armor
ourselves against the pervading
passage of time. Search for them

now. On nights when you can't
quite recall the ankle-twist
in that city, the pull to the edge

as the train passes by. It's a conversation
had between friends in the next second
of quiet. The text sits without life

in the interim of underground
and above. You like the places
between, but despise the word.

I won't write it now, because I wish
to suspend the sigh for a lifetime.
There is a forever in a sea-fever

smell of day-old anchovy babies bleeding
across the slice of pizza you never put away
in the fridge. But you toss the bites back

with whiskey. Try to find something smaller
than lying. The truth is, I don't need much
to lose your face

in a crowd. I need even less
to find your voice
in the back of my mind,

telling me all the ways
I've knotted people into impossibilities.
And yes, yes I know. I was never good

at math. But leaving.
This I've perfected. You can't follow
scattered steps from subway stations.

But maybe, try to remember
the flutter-squint lash-stuck
look I had that summer. You passed by

and said nothing. Some nights I forget
we're not owed the neon fight of after;
light flash of someone else's selfie.

We're all just weeded with shadow selves
we persuade to cartwheel off in the dark.
They take those crooked smiles

magicked into immortality.
They are us, but we'll never be
them again.

The
Tender
Slice of
Horizon

Alexandre Ferrere

A beam of light(
physical in dust
)becomes a movie.
        Minutes add
        to each other: soon
                        it's summertime.
                        Simple. Summer.
                        Blue
                                prints
                                        of next winters;
                        Blue
                                berries
                                        among splinters.

        "Prepare your lips
        for a pretty kiss";
    odd smiles.
Nothing lasts
    but ruins.
                        And there,
                        there, surreal, I saw a double
                        the double I come across
                        in places I've been before;
                        what distant sounds this ghost
                        would cry now that I'm going,
                                now that I'm gone?
        I haunt every former step taken
        and am haunted the same   by their echoes
                        their echoes
                                their   echoes.

Then I've stumbled in the church,
passed the ark,
but went out;
        took a look,
                above:
Here's a black backlit vivid bird.
Higher: a lazy plane fell into smoke.
Higher and *ailleurs*: a bleached star,
                        a dot of white light
                            trapped in ink.
Hours ended in a madness of squeaks
& spoke unknown syllables
mis/interpreted
mis/understood
blunt even in their false inter/
pretation:
predation of new
on old, on all.
        Paranoia adds a quality to time
        lightening each side
        of the current flow
        (cubist day).
            What to do?

                    Foreheads are cold
                    against the window
        Over   -   looking a warm river
                            of   tender
concrete:
            over   -   view of to   morrow.

Time is hunting hints, catching them in a finale corner:
Counting the days,
the sheep.
Here it comes; here comes to-   day
slaughtered
and exhausted. Here it comes; here comes to-   morrow
with a hangdog expression,
vital at first,
now aware, now afraid
to fulfill its duty, waiting
on the death row. If only . . .
"Here, here. Hush little baby,
I love you
I lov-

Yesterwhatever

Marlin Bressi

It began last summer during a snoozefest between the Phillies and Braves, on a hot August night in Atlanta with both teams out of playoff contention, no less. The Braves were up by one run—the only run of the game—and the Atlanta closer was able to preserve the shutout one-hitter, clenching the victory around ten o'clock. I clicked off the television and stumbled into bed with my wife.

"That was a quick game," Miranda muffled into her pillow.

"That's what I thought, too." I kicked off my shoes and whipped my flattened pillow into a foamy froth. "It was the strangest thing, Mir. I've watched paint dry with greater enthusiasm. Yet, you'd think it was a real barn burner."

Miranda rolled over onto her back and stated her opinion, over the squeaking of springs, that all baseball games were painfully boring to watch, whether the home team piled up one run or a hundred. "That's why I stopped watching after the third inning and went to bed," she added.

"You're missing the point, dear. Both teams changed pitchers so often that by the time the seventh inning stretch rolled around, there was a furrow from the bullpen to the mound," I said. "Then some drunken fan streaked across the outfield, causing a fifteen-minute delay. And yet, in spite of the delays and the lethargic pace, the game wrapped up on time. Nine fifty-seven, to be precise. Isn't that strange?"

My question was answered with a snore. After a few minutes of jockeying for a comfortable position, I joined my wife in slumber.

At the breakfast table the following morning, after downing three cups of coffee apiece, we both complained that it was hard to shake the sand out of our eyes. Though we had gotten nine hours of solid sleep, we felt like we were back in college, popping morning mints to mask our booze breath and staring bleary-eyed at a wobbling professor after three hours of shuteye.

The fuzziness persisted though morning, until Alex poked his shaggy head into my office and asked if I wanted to join him for lunch. "Isn't it a little early to be thinking about lunch?" I asked, glancing at my watch and noticing, to my utter amazement, that noon was just five minutes away. I felt not the slightest nag of hunger; I could feel an invisible patina of grease still lingering on my lips from my rushed breakfast of bacon. Chalking it up to imagination, I agreed to meet Alex across the street at Garibaldi's. The hour went by so quickly that we had to return back to the office before my club sandwich and Alex's salad emerged from the depths of the kitchen.

"This place has really gone downhill," Alex grumbled as we exited the restaurant into a hazy afternoon. "It's as if the entire waitstaff popped phenobarbital this morning."

"So you've noticed it, too!" My voice came out slightly more panicked than I had hoped. Suddenly afraid that my verbal ejaculation might have made me sound half out of my mind, I agreed that, yes, Garibaldi's was becoming a disappointment. "Let's try that new cafe on Front Street next time." Alex inquisitively raised a furry caterpillar of an eyebrow.

I will write more later. Must go to sleep.

"Travis, does it seem like time is going by faster than it used to?" asked Miranda over her shoulder one evening as she dried the dishes. Even though we have a ludicrously expensive dishwasher that has more cycles than Lance Armstrong's garage, my wife prefers to do the dishes by hand. Says it gives her time for some good, deep thinking.

"Well, you know what they say, honey," I answered from

behind the refrigerator door. "Time seems to pass more quickly when you get older."

Miranda rewarded me with a snap of a damp dishtowel to the behind. Our daughter, Allie, erupted in a gale of laughter, then scampered into the living room with a fistful of crayons and her half-colored hippopotamus.

"I'm being serious," Miranda said. "It's after eight, and I haven't even come close to finishing the laundry, not to mention a dozen other chores." I told Miranda that I tried to make the same point last night, but she had no recollection of the postgame conversation. "I guess I was more tired than I had realized."

We were not alone. In the coming weeks I would hear offhand remarks from several people about the confounding lapse of time, the missing minutes that somehow vanished as thoroughly as a drop of water on a hot skillet. In the grocery store I overheard a wife telling her husband that it was as if they had just been there, no more than a week earlier, but the disinterested husband was too focused on selecting a breakfast cereal to reply. One cloudy afternoon I walked past a young man standing on the corner who was passionately insisting into his phone that he had already paid the electric bill, and how could it possibly be due again so soon?

Of course, not everybody found themselves grappling with this peculiar dissociative fugue, and for every voice asking where the time had gone, another voice chimed a perfectly rational explanation: *You only think you were here last week. You're probably just experiencing a touch of déjà vu. It's all because of the summer solstice. Days are getting shorter, and that's why it feels like there is less time.*

Others simply shrugged and admitted to feeling no change at all.

One Sunday morning I woke up in the afternoon to ca-
cophonous clunking and raced downstairs to find Miranda in
the kitchen angrily chucking withered heads of lettuce and
moldy peaches into the trash.

"What's the matter?" I asked. She thrust a wilted stalk of
celery into my face like someone trying to ward off a demon
with a crucifix.

"Just look at this!" she barked. "I'm going to march right
up to the manager of the produce department and give him a
piece of my mind. Do you have any idea how much food we've
had to throw away this month?"

"Maybe the refrigerator is on the blink," I suggested fee-
bly. "Did we lose power last night?"

"No," she replied with a ferocious head shake. "Nothing
has thawed in the freezer."

By the end of September everyone at the office had noticed the change, though it was never addressed directly, in
much the same polite way you would never point out a stranger's obesity or a cousin's bad breath. Only Alex seemed un-
phased, or rather delighted, by the quickening. He had insisted that it only *felt* like time was speeding up because we were
getting into the busy season. He waltzed around the cubicles
making cash register noises, daydreaming of productivity bonuses.

But Alex was rudely awakened when Mr. Endicott called
us into the conference room one morning and read aloud the
third-quarter sales figures the way a speaker at a memorial ser-
vice reads a list of the dead. It was disheartening news because
we believed that we had been busy little beavers—it certainly
seemed like we had been busier. Mainly we were crestfallen
over the loss of our bonuses. Especially those of us who made
foolish and extravagant purchases on the assumption that we

had been shattering quotas. "I haven't seen such piss-poor pro-ductivity since the days of carbon copies and mimeographs!" bellowed Mr. Endicott. We all looked at each other, confused.

"I think that's some sort of machine that tells you wheth-er or not a mime is telling the truth," theorized Brayden Buchwald after the meeting, as we walked back to our desks humbled, hands in pockets and heads held low.

One Saturday afternoon in early November, I went down-town to Roy's Barber Shop for a trim.

"Back so soon, Travis? Seems like I just cut your hair a week ago."

"It's been two months, Roy," I reminded him.

The good thing about thinning hair is that it doesn't take very long to cut, yet the sun was already beginning to dip down below the buildings of Forsyth Street, painting the win-dow with shades of orange and magenta, when Roy pulled the thin paper strip from my neck and lowered the chair.

"Say, Roy, this might seem like a strange question, but how many haircuts do you do in a typical day?"

"Twenty, twenty-five maybe," he replied.

"And today?"

"Five."

"Business slow?"

"Not really." He sighed. "I guess these old hands aren't what they used to be."

It's time to go to bed again. I will write more tomorrow. Last night took seven days. How many times will the sun rise and set while we sleep this time?

It was the second week of November when I stopped going to work. Mr. Endicott had been urging us for weeks to keep a stiff upper lip—whatever that meant—and to soldier on. However, by the end of our shift (which now lasted three days) the upper lips we had shaved that morning had blossomed into prickly mustaches, and the soldiers began to go AWOL. "You still need a paycheck to survive!" he barked, while Alex and Brayden made for the door with their briefcases and Karen sobbed inconsolably with her head on the reception desk.

"What's the point?" I asked Mr. Endicott, removing my necktie and tossing it into the trash can. Money was no longer useful. No one was out there buying food. The looters had already taken it all, right down to the lima beans.

Each day went by faster and faster, like we were spinning madly out of control. Christmas was so brief that the entire day was dark, except for a thin sliver in the middle. Allie would be turning three in January; she didn't know any better to know that this was not normal. Upstairs, Miranda wept while Bing Crosby took four hours to sing "White Christmas." I caught a glimpse of myself in the mirror on top of the dresser. The face I had shaved that morning was bearded; my hair was once again over my ears. I put a hand on my wife's shoulder as she sobbed.

"Damn it, Travis," she said in a red-faced slobber, "soon there won't even be any point in taking down the Christmas tree."

"Honey, millions of brains bigger and better than ours are working on the problem," I said. I didn't know if it was true, but it had to be. "Whatever it is."

Miranda stood up and studied her reflection in the mirror. This ritual was something she did ten times a day, waiting for the gray hair, waiting to be greeted by the face of her mother. "Why won't they tell us anything? If only somebody would just *say* something!" She collapsed onto the mattress and, with trembling fingers, drew the covers over her chin. The morning sun was rising outside the window.

The brightest minds in the world had no answer. Geophysicists had stated repeatedly since Christmas that the Earth was not spinning faster on its axis. A century ago it was revolving at the speed of approximately 1,000 miles per hour, and it still is. The Earth's orbit around the sun still takes 365.256 days, they insisted, quelling rumors to the contrary but sparking a new wave of terrifying speculation in the aftermath. "This is not at all like the plot of a bad sci-fi movie," one scientist lectured gravely, in a sentence that took ten clicks of the clock's minute hand to speak. "There is no reason for time to be behaving—or misbehaving—in this fashion."

I must sleep again. When I wake up in the morning, it will be autumn. Morning is an archaic term; it now exists only as something that we had seen once. Miranda says that morning is a ghost. It's still there, you just have to be lucky enough to catch a glimpse.

I think in dreams, and dream in thought: Maybe the sun has collapsed and has shrunken to half its size and maybe, as a result, we have been pulled in closer, no longer 92.96 million miles away from the sun but 46.48 million miles away. No, that cannot make sense. Chronological age and biological age are two completely different things. At least that's what one of the experts on television said yesterday. Yesternight. Yesterwhatever.

If this is the case, then the truth may be that the problem is not in the stars at all, but in ourselves. In our blood. In our cells. Time is not moving faster—maybe we have all just slowed to a crawl. We are no longer on Eastern Standard Time or Coordinated Universal Time. Greenwich is burning

because yesterwhatever somebody torched the Royal Obser-
vatory, a feeble attempt to exact revenge on an enemy we can't
even begin to identify. We are on giant sequoia time now. Sail-
ing stone time, like those mysterious rocks in Death Valley
that crawl across the desert without explanation, moving an
inch or two each century and leaving behind a trail in the
sand older than religion.

Strangely, inexplicably, the effect of this madness on our
metabolism has been minimal. It is necessary to eat constant-
ly because we know that we will waste away if we don't, yet
we never feel hunger and we never feel full. Either our metabolism has acclimated to the change or we just don't feel
anything anymore, save for an overwhelming desire to sleep, a
craving for repose so sharp that it has become physically pain-
ful. We are trying to hold on to this whizzing, whirling carni-
val ride for dear life, which is diamond priceless and pebble
worthless at the same time.

There is not an ambulance outside; the light strobing
through the bedroom blinds (which now grow dusty in a matter of what I think are hours) is just the rising and setting of
the sun. In what I think was March, Allie began wearing her
mother's clothes.

"Goodwhatever," I say to my beloved Miranda with a
yawn. "I'll see you next year."

All of the scientists and politicians and generals turned to
mummies before they could solve this tragic riddle because the
quickening of time has affected our brain function more than
our metabolic rate. We can feel the expansion of our cerebral
ventricles; we can feel the plaque sticking to the gray matter
of our brains as surely as we used to feel the soles of our shoes
sticking to the surface of a freshly blacktopped parking lot on

a summer afternoon. Outside, men and women are toppling like trees, lumberjacked by hypothalamus inflammation.

Allie, Miranda, and I made a pact not to fall asleep. Sleep is deadly, we agreed, because each sleep period now lasts several seasons. We could die of heatstroke or hypothermia while we slumbered helplessly in bed, shivering or sweating depending on which of the five stages of sleep we were in.

The second hands and minute hands have now broken off the clocks, and the hour hands spin with reckless disregard for timekeeping, a pinwheel in an unrelenting breeze. With the blinds drawn the rising and setting of the sun produces a steady flickering much like the inside of a projection room at an old-fashioned movie theater and, though it is never spoken, we all know that the show is over.

Last week I could look in the mirror and watch my hair grow like time-lapse photography, but to shave now would be as utterly ridiculous as trying to swallow the ocean one salty teaspoon at a time.

Our vow to stay awake has been shattered like physics because our circadian rhythms are lost orphans, confused and wandering. I rest my throbbing head on the cool pillow, hot pillow, cold pillow and kiss my white-haired wife, who now creaks with arthritis and has lost all but four of her teeth since morning. But she is still unspeakably beautiful in my eyes, which are failing rapidly. "Goodmonth, goodyear, goodwhatever, my love," I croak like an ancient bullfrog, planting a parched kiss on her soft forehead.

Cadenza

James Penha

No more meds, my aunt tells me
on Christmas. *I was alone all day,*
and of course it's so, the caregiver
with her own family and I half a world
away. *I'm ninety-seven. Ninety-seven!*
She's ninety-five. An amazing ninety-
five on her own in her own apartment
still. Still. But who's counting? *One hundred?*
I don't want to be one hundred. Of course
I tell her you do and I do but who am I
to understand now how ponderous
the years make the hours she wakes
and waits for the next meal swallowed
without relish, the next toilet without
ease, the next phone call from a nephew
for whom she usually tries to smile.

An Old Photo

Maina Chen

One picture is all it takes
to bring back the warmth in your words
and the kindness in your laughter.

One picture is all it takes
to see your toothy, crooked smile and
thick, calloused hands that tell stories of a life without riches.
Proudly, they display the scars you earned in the fields.

One picture is all it takes
to make your daughter's eyes glisten from something that isn't
tears
and for her to breathe out a lifetime's worth of praise.
To see the strongest woman I know
with a crack in her armor.

One picture is all it takes
for me to go back to that summer when I met you,
and you beamed with energy as if you were the sun incarnate.

One picture is all it takes
to remember the scorching heat outside your home
where you rested beneath your fruit trees,
reclined in an aged porch swing.
You called me over and as we sunk deeper into our hideaway,
time slowed and slipped out of our reach.
The stars came out to greet us,
with every fleeting tale you whispered
through thin lips and fluttering eyes.

You didn't talk for long,
Because you knew I floated in a world of few words
And didn't feel the need to intrude in it.

One picture is all it takes
for me to forget that you are human, too.
And that in your exuded radiance
you might one day fall.
And even though I met you once
in a summer gone many years ago,
know that I'll always love you,
and that we'll meet again in our hideaway,
someday.

time slowed and slipped

out of our reach

Elsie

Denny Jace

You'd shown me a list: Elsie's itinerary. I was grateful you'd not called it "bucket."

    1. Lick a slug.

(You thought it might give you a high; I worried about the hygiene. When it came to it, I'd say you spat more than licked.)

    2. Dye hair pink.

("It was falling out," you said, "so I've shaved it all off." Then you handed me a pot of pink paint and a brush. With each stroke I felt the rough clumps of stubble clinging to your scalp, and the hope I held tight fell away.)

Today is a good day. We are in a private room—"very posh," you'd said. You are sitting up, as pale as the sheets and as small as a child, but your eyes are bright and your smile wide. You weave your brittle fingers through my mine; icy cotton threads I could snap with a curl of my palm.

"Take me back there," you say, your eyes searching my face, seeking accord. For a moment I'm lost . . . do you mean home? Before you were sick? The other hospital? And then I realize, and I am winded with such a forceful blow that a physical ache doubles me over. The list. You mean number four:

    4. Climb our mountain.

(Indonesia, where we'd backpacked, and I'd proposed.)

The weight of pretence pulls my gaze from you. "Definitely! Once you're back on your feet," I say. And then you say, "promise me," and so I do.

Green grass as far as I can see, fresh new shoots of life. It's the rainy season yet still temperatures soar, and humidity thickens the air.

"We're here," I whisper, my arms wrapped tightly around you, my world in a small black box.

I tilt my face up to the sky, the sun's warmth cupping my face. Mist moistens the sky, cleansing the mountain's clouds; flowers sway and scent the air as, into the breeze, I release you.

Your kisses, laughter and love, swirl and dance; silver fairy dust; you float away on the breeze.

I release   you

The Widow

<hr>

Kendra Nuttall

My mother blossomed
after my father's death.

Don't get me wrong,
she was always a spider killer and

a mean pastelito maker, but
somewhere between the funeral potatoes

and the daily Diet Coke,
God spoke:

You don't have to
cook dinner for a man every day.

Don't sit in the cancer
hospital waiting for words

that will never come.
Don't hold a cold hand

when you could hold
me. Please.

She believed in God.
I believed in her

and pastelitos with cheese
on the backyard swing.

She got a full-time job
with insurance and time off

and a brand-new bedroom
where the sun shines on yellow.

She dances with neighbors
to department store sales

and dances alone '
to La Bamba,

but it's not sad anymore.
Por ti seré, for you I'll be.

It was the only song
my father sang.

My mother sings to me.
For you I'll be.

My mother sings to me

for you I'll be

Summers on Repeat

Maina Chen

I.
I've listened and looped for
the same few wordless songs.
Nostalgia pours into my ears,
one lamp to illuminate my way.

Nothing soothes me more
than the nighttime breeze in summer.
The in-between of blazing suns
and a missing sun.

II.
A bittersweet honey
spent pining for days of wasted freedom when I was younger
to the days when I was so free I was wracked with boredom.
When I could audibly hear silence
a dull buzzing that clings to the eardrum
dull enough that I could blink hard and refocus on
a slow metronome clock and it'd disappear.

How it nibbled at my toes,
and how I, suspended in animation,
sought the light of my lamp and my own comfort
when the world and those around it were quiet,
asleep.

III.
Nostalgia in the scent of a flower
I'd imagine swirling in from the same window by my bedside
calming, slightly sweet and reminding me of my mother's smile

from when she used to be happy,
looking at her favorite pure white jasmine.
In a denim dress and straw hat, her hair pulled into a short ponytail
a young, bright woman of twenty-so years.
Just as she was in the picture we found when we went digging.
I imagined it'd be lavender
formerly her favorite color.

Nostalgia comes to me
in the form of ten summers long gone
and a flower whose name
I will never know.

**I could audibly hear silence
a dull buzzing**

Sailing

Emma Keanie

the mellifluous
                honeyed tones
                of the bee
                            bumble into
        a felt choir   of summer ecstasy
            thoughts swarm
            with the thick
                    h a z e
            swimming
        into lighter
scenes
            losing noise   while
                                        gaining quiet
                                melody
                        melting
                    as one
            with hums
            sweet scents
            perfumes of sea sounds

                            sailing as summer

Shifts

Emma Keanie

cloud-veils depart
with   *dissolving*
          motion
             while   frost-tips s
                                    l
                                    i
                                    p
                           into inexistence
softening time
u
  n
    f
      o
        l
          d
            s
              into summer
                       the porcupine pricks
                       of pandemic
                       assaulting psyche
                  f i z z l e
             and
           f
         a
      d
    e
backward into
shades of memory

                           》》

daffodils in repose
now hibiscus *throws*
              light
     upon summer

                              blush hues
                         mingling
        with the kisses
        of cool breezes
                   segueing
                         with the salt spray
              tasted by glancing the
              glimmer of seas

        unblind to beauty
        in fecundity

                                   and airy bliss
                                   of liberty
     not unfelt in heart
                    summer swells

summer swells

The Grass
Was Long
and Soft

Steve Denehan

The world is smaller now
because I make it small
but back then
at thirteen
on a late summer Saturday
it was infinite
a never ending
forever thing

except that
my knocks went unanswered
or were met with mothers' faces
telling me that Bob was sick
that Damien was not around
that Maura was off with her father
on that late summer Saturday
it was just me

I walked
down to the pinkeen pond
but the older boys were there
and one of them had destroyed my new bike that summer
for no reason at all
(fifteen years later, blind drunk
he would crash into my parked car
writing it off
what a guy)

I walked the couple of miles to the cinema
but there was nothing showing

nothing good at least
I got a bag of chips
extra salt
extra vinegar
extra crispy bits

arrived back at the green
sure that there would be a match
a game of some sort
it was empty
but the grass was long and soft
and felt just fine when I lay upon it
put my feet up on the low wall
and watched the sky
and I think that was the first time
I knew
really knew
I was going to be alright

the world is
smaller now

September Sadness

Dani Castonzo

The Amtrak 370 won't get you there on time, but maybe you'll get the seat to yourself. Guided by the lake, the dunes, the leaves just on the verge of yellowing but summer's not gone yet. Two girls in white gowns watching from the church's open mouth, fireworks for sale, Cindy or Mary or Luna's Diner with the windowful of Sunday morning regulars. Redamak's is still open, but you haven't been since family car rides weren't heavy with silence.

You've smelled the Midwest green a thousand times but you never quite recall it in January.

On the train in your own seat while the rest of the car sleeps. One day your friends will stop calling and your parents won't be waiting at the pizza place when the train pulls in. You'll lay alone in your childhood bunk bed and listen to the house creak at night, echoes of the family that used to fill the silence. How many times can you push someone away before they stop trying, you wonder, as the train creeps through yellow wildflowers and infinite prairie grasses. Fall threatens, with crisp nights and falling leaves, and even the most beautiful summer nights are somber because it won't last.

You are breaking but maybe you'll make it through one more train ride.

September sadness is watching summer fade away and knowing each season there are fewer people to call. You can't stop it so give it a warm farewell; knees in the dirt, heat rising through your back, one final whistle as the train sinks in the setting sun.

Contributors

Stacy Alderman has writing featured in *Potato Soup Journal*, *Heart and Humanity*, *HerStry*, *The Mighty*, and *Hometown Odyssey*. She blogs about mental health at *Quirky, Confused, & Curvy* and lives near Pittsburgh with her husband and fur kid. When she's not writing or reading, she's probably watching hockey or (thinking about) traveling.

Akhim Alexis is a writer born and raised in Trinidad and Tobago. He is currently pursuing an MA in literatures in English at the University of the West Indies at St. Augustine. His most recent work has appeared in *Moko*, *In Parentheses*, and *KAIROS Literary Magazine* and is forthcoming in *The Caribbean Writer*.

Marlin Bressi is the author of four nonfiction books, including *Hairy Men in Caves: True Stories of America's Most Colorful Hermits* (Sunbury Press, 2015) and *Pennsylvania Oddities* (Sunbury Press, 2018).

Dani Castonzo is a fundraiser and creative writer from Chicago. She is an avid reader, traveler, and walker. She frequently performs in Chicago's live storytelling and improv scene.

Maina Chen is a nerd masquerading as an editor and writer in some cavernous corner of Brooklyn. A half-nocturnal night dweller, she writes short stories and poems. When she's not creating monsters, she's battling them in video games. Her work has appeared in *The Well*, *Ape-X*, *Catan Stories: Legend of the Sea Robbers*, *Youth-for-Youth: Mental Health Guidebook*, *NextShark*, and more.

Linda M. Crate has work published in numerous magazines and anthologies both online and in print. She is the author of six poetry chapbooks, the latest of which is *More Than Bone Music* (Clare Songbirds Publishing House, 2019). She's also the author of the novel *Phoenix Tears* (Czykmate Books, 2018). Recently she has published two full-length poetry collections, *Vampire Daughter* (Dark Gatekeeper Gaming, February 2020) and *The Sweetest Blood* (Cyberwit, February 2020).

Sarra Culleno is a London born, Manchester-based UK poet, a mother of two, and an English teacher. She performs at open mic poetry events and slams across the United Kingdom. She writes about children's rights, motherhood, identity, technology, the environment, politics, modern monogamy, and the education system. Sarra has work published by *Les Femmes Folles*, *Three Drops from a Cauldron*, *Hidden Voice Publishing Anthology: Volume 1*, *Bonnie's Crew Press*, and *Bollocks to Brexit* anthology. She was longlisted for the Cinnamon Press Pamphlet Prize and appears as featured poet at Herstories Festival, The Festival of Manchester, Write Out Loud Sale, WatchWord at Chorlton Book Festival, and others. Sarra appeared as special guest poet in the Manchester Fringe Festival show STREETLIGHTS + fairylights at the Hope Aria Academy. You can find readings on her YouTube channel, accessible through her Instagram and Twitter profiles. You can find her on Twitter at @sarra1978, on Instagram at @sarracullenopoetry, and on Facebook at facebook.com/sarracullenopoetry.

Uttaran Das Gupta is a New Delhi-based writer and journalist. He teaches at O.P. Jindal Global University, Haryana, and frequently writes on cinema, poetry, and politics. He recently published a novel, *Ritual*.

Steve Denehan lives in Kildare, Ireland, with his wife Eimear and daughter Robin. He is the author of *Miles of Sky Above Us, Miles of Earth Below* (Cajun Mutt Press), *Of Thunder, Pearls and Birdsong* (Fowlpox Press), *Living in the Core of an Apple* (Analog Submission Press), and *A Chandelier of Beating Hearts* (forthcoming from Salmon Poetry). He won Irish Times' New Irish Writing twice, and his numerous publication credits include *Poetry Ireland Review, Acumen, Westerly,* and *Into the Void.* He has been nominated for Best of the Net and Best New Poet and has been twice nominated for the Pushcart Prize.

Alexandre Ferrere is twenty-nine and lives in France. After a master's degree in library sciences and a master's degree in English literature, he is now working on a PhD on American poetry. His essays and poems have appeared or are forthcoming in *Beatdom, Empty Mirror, Rust + Moth, Lumin Journal, Riggwelter Press, Barren Magazine, Isacoustic, armarolla, Lucent Dreaming, Kissing Dynamite, Porridge Magazine,* and elsewhere.

John Grey is an Australian poet, US resident. Recently published in *Sin Fronteras, The Dalhousie Review,* and *Qwerty* with work upcoming in *Plainsongs, Willard and Maple,* and *Connecticut River Review.*

Denny Jace has been writing since June 2019. She writes flash fiction and short stories and is building up to her first novel. She lives in Shropshire with her husband and two (grownup) children. Most of her days are spent reading her stories to Maude and Stanley, her two faithful dogs. She has been published in *Ellipsis Zine,* and her flash fiction "When the Last Flame Is Blown" won Retreat West's Micro Fiction Competition in January 2020.

Elizabeth Jaeger has had essays, short stories, book reviews, and poetry published in various print and online journals, including *Watchung Review, The Doctor T. J. Eckleburg Review, Ovunque Siamo, Peacock Journal, Boston Accent,* and *Italian Americana.* An excerpt from her novel in progress is forthcoming in *Newtown Literary.* Jaeger recently founded *Maple Tiger Review,* an online journal dedicated to publishing work written by teens and tweens. She is the book reviews editor at *Ovunque Siamo.* When Jaeger isn't reading or writing, she enjoys going hiking and taking road trips with her son. Her website is jaegerwrites13.wordpress.com.

Sarah Jane Justice is a creative whose work has been commended in a variety of fields. She performed at the Sydney Opera House as a national finalist in the 2018 Australian Poetry Slam, counts four professional releases of original music to her name, wrote and performed a one-woman cabaret show for the 2016 Adelaide Fringe, and makes regular appearances around South Australia as a storyteller and spoken word artist. Her poetry and prose have been featured in publications around the world, including releases from *The Blue Nib, Black Hare Press,* and *South Broadway Ghost Society.*

Emma Keanie is a PhD researcher in Samuel Beckett studies at the University of Reading. She has a master of arts and bachelor of arts in English literature from Ulster University and is a reviewer for *The Beckett Circle.* Emma is interested in the shapes and sounds of poetry, how thoughts can drift silently staining the page.

Kayla King is the author of *These Are the Women We Write About,* a microcollection of poetry published by The Poetry

Annals. Kayla's fiction and poetry has been published by or is forthcoming from *Firewords Magazine, Sobotka Literary Magazine, Fearsome Critters, Barren Magazine,* and *Honey & Lime,* among others. You can follow Kayla's writing journey over on her website at kaylakingbooks.com or her twitterings at @KaylaMKing.

Sarah Marquez is an MA candidate at Southern New Hampshire University. She has work published and forthcoming in various magazines and journals, including *Amethyst Review, Crépe & Penn, Ink&Nebula, peculiars magazine,* and *Royal Rose.* When not writing, she can be found reading, sipping coffee, or tweeting at @Sarahmarissa338.

A. Martine is a trilingual writer, musician, and artist of color who goes where the waves take her. She might have been a kraken in a past life. She's an assistant editor at *Reckoning Press* and a managing editor of *The Nasiona.* Her collection of poems *At Sea* was shortlisted for the 2019 Kingdoms in the Wild Poetry Prize. Some words are found or forthcoming in *Berfrois, The Rumpus, Bright Wall/Dark Room, Metaphorosis, South Broadway Ghost Society, RIC Journal, Lamplight, TERSE. Journal, Gone Lawn, Truancy Magazine, Crack the Spine, The Confessionalist Zine, Ghost City Review, Rogue Agent, Boston Accent, Porridge Magazine, Camwood Lit, Feminine Collective,* and *Anti-Heroin Chic.* Follow her on Twitter at @Maelllstrom, and you can find her online at maelllstrom.com.

Mark Martyre is a Canadian writer and musician. He has written and produced six full-length studio albums since 2012, as well as music written and performed for theater. His music has garnered critical acclaim and attention nationally and internationally, and he has toured across Canada and Europe. In 2019, Mark also published a collection of his poems, *Notes on Torn Sheets*, and has also had several poems published in online journals and literary magazines.

Michelle M. Mead is a writer from Upstate New York. She has edited, written (stories, poetry, reviews), illustrated, and interviewed for two print zines, *Artless & Naked* and *Whimsy*. She has been published in various print magazines, including *Polluto*, *The Thirty First Bird Review*, *Trespass*, *Blinking Cursor*, *Cross Stitch Crazy*, *Words@Deakin Press*, and *Chronogram*, and ezines, including *Gutter Eloquence*, *EMG Zine*, *Apparatus*, and *Under the Juniper Tree*. She has also published two poetry books, *Moongirls and Nightdreams* and *Divided Together* (lulu.com). She is working on multiple novels and a poetry collection.

Kendra Nuttall is a copywriter by day and poet by night. Her work has previously appeared in *Spectrum Literary Journal*, *Capsule Stories*, and *Chiron Review*, among others. She lives in Utah with her husband and dog. Find more of her work on kendranuttall.com.

Bruce Pemberton is a retired high school teacher, coach, and Gulf War veteran. His most recent work has appeared in *American Life in Poetry*, *Third Wednesday*, *Sky Island Journal*, *Ocotillo Review*, *Streetlight Magazine*, and *iTeach Literary Magazine* and the anthologies *In Tahoma's Shadow* and *Spokane Writes*. He lives on the Palouse in rural eastern Washington.

James Penha, a native New Yorker, has lived for the past quarter-century in Indonesia. He has been nominated for Pushcart Prizes in fiction and poetry, and his verse appeared in 2019 in *Headcase: LGBTQ Writers & Artists on Mental Health and Wellness* (Oxford University Press), *Lovejets: Queer Male Poets on 200 Years of Walt Whitman* (Squares and Rebels), and *What Remains: The Many Ways We Say Goodbye* (Gelles-Cole). His essays have appeared in the *New York Daily News* and the *New York Times*. Penha edits *The New Verse News*, an online journal of current events poetry. You can find him on Twitter at @JamesPenha.

Larry Pike has poetry and fiction published in *The Louisville Review*, *Seminary Ridge Review*, *Caesura*, *Exposition Review*, and *Vitamin ZZZ*, among other publications. He has work forthcoming in *Jelly Bucket*. He lives in Glasgow, Kentucky.

Kali Richmond is a native Londoner and lapsed video artist currently attempting a closer to nature existence in the north of England. When not cultivating an unruly patch of land and unrulier children, she writes about vulnerability and isolation. Her work will soon be featured in *Kanstellation* and *Idle Ink*.

Brian Rihlmann was born in New Jersey and resides in Reno, Nevada. He writes free verse poetry and has been published in *The Blue Nib*, *The American Journal of Poetry*, *Cajun Mutt Press*, *The Rye Whiskey Review*, and others. His first poetry collection, *Ordinary Trauma*, was published by Alien Buddha Press in 2019.

Morgan Russell is a rhetorician, poet, and the creative writing editor for *Marías at Sampaguitas*. Her work may be found in a number of places. (Visit linktr.ee/morgankrussell.) When she's not reading or writing, she can be found mainlining coffee and mimosas or working in web support until she becomes Fully Realized and transcends this plane of existence (i.e., is able to move out of her dad's house and go to grad school).

Ed Ruzicka was raised beside creeks and cornfields not far from Chicago and now lives with his wife, Renee, and their doddering bulldog, Tucker, in Baton Rouge. Ed has published one full-length volume and recently had his second, *My Life in Cars*, accepted for release. Ed's poems have appeared in *Atlanta Review*, *Rattle*, and *New Millennium Writings*, as well as many other literary journals and anthologies. More at edrpoet.com.

Lynne Schmidt is a mental health professional and an award-winning poet and memoir author who also writes young adult fiction. An avid snowboarder following her abortion experience, she is also an ambassador for Coalition Snow. She is the author of the poetry chapbooks *Gravity* (Nightingale and Sparrow Press, 2019) and *On Becoming a Role Model* (Thirty West, 2020). Her work has received the Maine Nonfiction Award and Frost Meadow Review's Editor's Choice Award, and she was a 2018 and 2019 Pacific Northwest Writers Association finalist for memoir and poetry respectively. Lynne is a five-time 2019 Best of the Net nominee and an honorable mention for the Charles Bukowski Prize for Poetry. In 2012 she started the project AbortionChat, which aims to lessen the stigma around abortion. When given the choice, Lynne prefers the company of her three dogs and one cat to humans.

Arianna Sebo (she/her) is a queer poet and writer living in Southern Alberta with her husband, pug, and five cats. Their home is brimming with cat posts, pet beds, fur, and love. She received her BA in philosophy from the University of Calgary, working in the field of law to feed her family and writing poetry to feed her philosophical soul. Her poetry can be found in *Kissing Dynamite*, *The Coachella Review*, *Front Porch Review*, and *45 Poems of Protest: The Pandemic*. Follow her at AriannaSebo .com and @AriannaSebo on Twitter and Instagram.

Lucy Tyrrell writes poems that are primarily inspired by nature and wild landscapes, outdoor pursuits, family stories, and travel. In 2016, after sixteen years in Alaska, she traded a big mountain (Denali) for a big lake (Lake Superior). Lucy lives near Bayfield, Wisconsin. Her favorite verbs to live by are "experience" and "create." She is Bayfield's Poet Laureate for 2020–2021.

Gillian Webster lives in the beautiful Georgian New Town of Edinburgh. She fell in love with the United States when she first began traveling there as a teenager. America has inspired her writing ever since. She has a BA (Hons) in marketing, French, and Italian from the University of Strathclyde and has taken classes in creative writing at The University of Edinburgh. Her first novel, *Donor #149*, was a finalist in the Penguin Random House Daily Mail First Crime Novel Award. She is working on her second novel, a domestic thriller set on the Upper West Side of Manhattan. In addition to writing, Gillian is an avid photographer. You can find her images on Instagram at @small_acts_of_sabotage_.

Editorial Staff

Natasha Lioe, Founder and Publisher

Natasha Lioe graduated with a BA in narrative studies from University of Southern California. She's always had an affinity for words and stories and emotions. Her work has appeared in *Adsum Literary Magazine* and *Capsule Stories*, and she won the Edward B. Moses Creative Writing Competition in 2016. Her greatest strength is finding and focusing the pathos in an otherwise cold world, and she hopes to help humans tell their unique, compelling stories.

Carolina VonKampen, Publisher and Editor in Chief

Carolina VonKampen graduated with a BA in English and history from Concordia University, Nebraska and completed the University of Chicago's editing certificate program. She is available for hire as a freelance copyeditor and book designer. For more information on her freelance work, visit carolina vonkampen.com. Her writing has appeared in *So to Speak*'s blog, *FIVE:2:ONE*'s #thesideshow, *Moonchild Magazine*, and *Déraciné Magazine*. Her short story "Logan Paul Is Dead" was nominated by *Dream Pop Journal* for the 2018 Best of the Net. She tweets about editing at @carolinamarie_v and talks about books she's reading on Instagram at @carolinamariereads.

Submission Guidelines

Capsule Stories **is a print literary magazine** published once every season. Our first issue was published on March 1, 2019, and we accept submissions year-round.

Become published in a literary magazine run by like-minded people. We have a penchant for pretty words, an affinity to the melancholy, and an undeniably time-ful aura. We believe that stories exist in a specific moment, and that that moment is what makes those stories unique.

What we're really looking for are stories that can touch the heart. Stories that come from the heart. Stories about love, identity, the self, the world, the human condition. Stories that show what living in this world as the human you are is like.

We accept short stories, poems, and remarkably written essays. For short stories and essays, we're interested in pieces under 3000 words. You may include up to five poems in a single poetry submission, and please send only one story or essay at a time. Please send previously unpublished work only, and only submit to one category at a time. Simultaneous submissions are okay, but please let us know if your submission is accepted elsewhere. Please include a brief third-person bio with your submission, and attach your submission in a Word document (no PDFs, please!).

You can email your submission to us at submissions@capsulestories.com.

Connect with us!
capsulestories.com
@CapsuleStories on Twitter and Facebook
@CapsuleStoriesMag on Instagram

CPSIA information can be obtained
at www.ICGtesting.com
Printed in the USA
LVHW020036170620
658107LV00012B/580